Contents

*G = gold; P = platinum

The Abercrombies

Philip Harper

AB 3036

Lara's Lament

Philip Sparke

AB 3036

Southern Swing

Mike Revell

AB 3036

The Ghost

John Miller

* Optional mutes throughout

AB 3036

Rondeau

from *Abdelazar*

Purcell arr. Nick Breeze

No Sir!

Kenneth Hesketh
(after English folksong)

Triple Tango

Stephen Roberts

AB 3036

Musketeers

Philip Sparke

AB 3036

A Birthday Fugue

Op. 176j

Derek Bourgeois

AB 3036

Proclamation

Kenneth Hesketh

AB 3036

Regally Cool!

Andrew Tyrrell

AB 3036

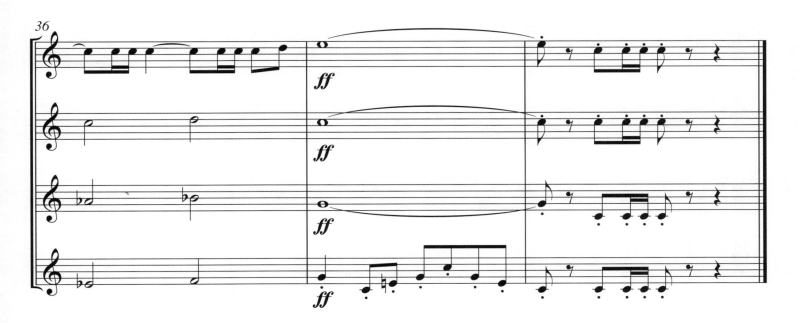

Love Song

Philip Sparke

AB 3036

La Cucaracha

Trad. arr. Stephen Roberts

Cucaracha Cockroach

Walking Balkan Brass

Chris Batchelor

AB 3036

The Earl of Oxford's March

Byrd arr. John Miller

AB 3036